THE GIRL
with the
SHOEBOX
LUNCH

written by
Sharon Russell
illustrated by Mark Brayer

This book is dedicated
to the memory of my mother,
Delores Morrison.
This was her story
and I feel privileged to share it.

It was a beautiful sunny day as an eight-year-old Delores (lovingly known as Dee Dee) waited anxiously for her dad to finish getting dressed.

Today was a super special day. Once a year,
Dee Dee would go to her dad's workplace.
He worked at a trainyard and it was
very exciting to visit there.

Aside from visiting her dad's workplace,
this was the only day that she got to eat
a very special lunch prepared by her mom.

Dee Dee had prepared for the day,
and really enjoyed the time she spent
decorating her shoebox lunch box.
She used crayons, markers, and stickers.

The best part of this day is that she would
get to eat her meal from the shoebox she had
decorated a few days earlier.

Her mom had prepared her favorite dishes-
two chicken wings, a small container of potato
salad, a fruit punch juice box, a roll, an apple,
and a slice of double chocolate cake.

As they headed for the trainyard, they passed huge weeping willow trees and rows of alfalfa, swaying in the wind.

The closer they got to their destination,
she could hear the sounds of the
train horns blaring.

As they pulled into the trainyard, Dee Dee
began to smile while gazing at the freight
and passenger cars.

Dee Dee wanted to know if she could look inside some of the cars. She especially liked the older passenger cars.

Dad said, "Of course," with a knowing smile as he had something in mind that would excite his daughter even more than just looking inside the cars.

As they walked around the yard, they stopped and talked to a few engineers that worked with Dee Dee's dad.

Dee Dee had lots of questions about the different types of trains and where they might be headed. Moreover, she also kept thinking about when she would be able to eat her very special lunch.

A few hours had passed, and Dee Dee's dad asked if she was ready to eat. She said, "Yes dad, I am very hungry."

Both Dee Dee and dad headed toward the car where Dee Dee thought they were going to eat their lunch.

As they approached their car, her dad stopped and said, "You know what, I have a much better place for us to eat lunch. "Where?" asked Dee Dee.

Dad said, "Just follow me, I have a surprise for you." Dee Dee didn't think the day could get any better. As they walked toward an old, rusty freight car, her dad walked around it, to the other side. There stood a beautiful, shiny vintage dining car, straight out of a movie!

"How 'bout we eat on this car?"
prompted Dee Dee's dad. "Can we really
eat on it?" asked Dee Dee.
"We certainly can," said her dad.
She marveled at all of the authentic-looking
seats, drapes, place settings,
and fancy dinnerware.

It was finally time to eat her very special shoebox lunch. As she unpacked her meal, she said, "This is a super-special place to eat my super-special lunch with my super-special dad."

And that is exactly what she did!

Sharon Russell is a debut author who felt compelled to share this charming story with the world. It was told to her and her sister Carol when they were young, by their mother whom they lost in 2020, about a very special day in her life.

CPSIA information can be obtained
at www.ICGtesting.com
Printed in the USA
BVHW020739010921
615710BV00022B/205